# DISNEY's Winnie the Pooh

## Annual 2000

**Editor:** Lisa Carless • **Designer:** Jonathan Gilbert

© Disney. Based on the Pooh stories by A.A. Milne. © The Pooh Properties Trust.
Published in Great Britain in1999 by Egmont World Ltd, Deanway Technology Centre,
Wilmslow Road, Handforth, Cheshire SK9 3FB. Printed in Italy. ISBN 0-7498-4252-0.

£5.99
UK Only

# Hello, boys and girls!

Welcome to the Hundred Acre Wood with Winnie the Pooh and all his friends. Why don't you join in the fun and games?

We've hidden lots of little objects throughout your annual - see if you can find them all. Put a tick over the objects in the boxes when you have found them. The numbers at the side of each picture tell you how many are hidden.

# Contents

# Flooded out!

**1** It had been raining when Piglet went to bed and it was still raining when he woke up. "I've never seen so much rain," he said.

**2** "I'll go and see what Pooh thinks of all the rain," Piglet thought. He put on his raincoat and hat, picked up his umbrella and set off.

**3** But as soon as he opened the front door to go out, water gushed into his house! "Oh, my gosh!" he cried. "It's a flood!" Piglet quickly grabbed hold of his umbrella.

**4** The umbrella fell upside-down in the water and Piglet splashed into it. Then the flood carried him off through the Hundred Acre Wood.

**5** Piglet floated all the way to Pooh's house in his umbrella boat. Pooh was sitting outside, on a branch, holding a pot of honey.

**6** "Jump in here, Pooh!" Piglet shouted. So Pooh jumped. He landed in the umbrella boat with such a splash Piglet almost fell out.

**7** "Oh bother, I've lost my honey pot!" cried Pooh. "And I almost lost me!" said Piglet. Then they noticed that the umbrella was sinking.

**8** "The flood is coming into the umbrella," said Pooh, worriedly, so they quickly used their hats to bail the water out.

**9** Then they sailed off again. "I do wish I could find my honey," sighed Pooh, peering into the water. "It was my very last pot." But Piglet was too busy worrying about something else!

**10** Just then, the umbrella boat bumped into the 'something else' that Piglet had been worrying about. Pooh and Piglet were thrown out straight on to...

**11** ...dry land! "Oh, there you are, Pooh and Piglet," said Christopher Robin who had been looking for them. "I was worried about you!"

**12** Then something rolled into Pooh. It was his pot of honey! "And I was worried about my honey. But it's here now, too!" smiled Pooh. They all laughed.

# Drawing with Piglet

Piglet is drawing faces in the raindrops.
Can you help him? You can copy the face
Piglet has drawn, or make up your own.

# Tigger's action rhyme

Say the rhyme, then do the actions, copying Tigger and Roo.

The Hundred Acre
Wood is flooded,
There's water everywhere,
But Tigger jumps upon a log,
And paddles without a care.

"Come and join me!" he shouts.
"Water's fun, you know!"
Roo jumps on the log
behind him,
Splash! Then off they go!

# Rabbit's maze

Rabbit is dreaming that he's going to the moon. With your finger trace which path he should take. Then count how many stars he passes on the way.

How many stars are there altogether?

# Trumpet trouble

**1** Owl was fast asleep when a loud noise woke him up. "What's that?" he gasped, jumping up and knocking his lamp over.

**2** The shade fell off the lamp and on to Owl's head. "Oh, dear, what's going on?" said Owl. "Everything's gone dark!"

**3** He pulled the lampshade off. Then he looked out of the window to see who was making the terrible noise. It was Tigger trying to play a trumpet! "Go away!" shouted Owl.

**4** So Tigger went off, still blowing his trumpet. Soon, he saw Piglet just about to hang out his washing. He crept up behind him and blew his trumpet really loudly. "Aaagh!" cried Piglet.

**5** Piglet was so shocked, he dropped his basket. The washing fell out and blew away. "My washing!" cried Piglet. He and Tigger ran after it all.

**6** The washing whirled and twirled, trying to get away. But Tigger was too fast. "Got it!" he shouted, jumping on a towel.

14

**7** At last, they caught everything except a sock. Then Tigger sat down to play his trumpet again. But no sound came out. "It's broken!" he said.

**8** Tigger took a big breath and blew really, really hard. "Parrrp!" A sock blew out straight at Piglet. "My sock!" said a muffled voice!

**9** Just then, Owl came along. He was surprised to see Piglet and Tigger looking very worn out. "Blowing a trumpet is hard work!" gasped Tigger.

# Piglet's colouring

Colour this picture with your crayons. Look at the little picture to see which colours to use.

What is Tigger doing?

How many socks is Piglet holding?

What colour is Tigger's trumpet?

What is your favourite musical instrument?

17

# The birthday party

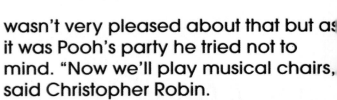

"Are you sitting comfortably, Pooh?" asked Christopher Robin. "Then I'll tell you a story."

Christopher Robin organised lots of games for Pooh and all his friends to play. First of all they played pass the parcel.
"Oh, goody! Tiggers love pass the parcel!" said Tigger. "I bet I win this game!"
But he didn't. Pooh did. His prize was a lovely big lollipop. Tigger wasn't very pleased about that but as it was Pooh's party he tried not to mind. "Now we'll play musical chairs," said Christopher Robin.
"Goody, Tiggers love musical chairs," said Tigger. "I bet I win this game!"
But he didn't. Rabbit did. He won a big red balloon. Tigger wasn't very pleased about that.
Then they played pin the tail on the donkey. Eeyore won that. His prize was a bright yellow ribbon. And Piglet won hunt the parcel. His prize was a party blower that made a very loud noise. Tigger wasn't very pleased about that. In fact, he was so cross he refused to play any more games. He sat down in a corner of the wood with his back to everyone and sulked. Tigger had been sulking for at least

ten minutes when he heard
Christopher Robin shout.
"So the winner is ...TIGGER!" Tigger was
surprised! Pooh shouted, "Come and
get your prize, Tigger!" Tigger turned
around. "But I can't have won. I didn't
join in the game," he said sadly.

"Yes you did," said Pooh. "We were
playing musical statues and you kept
still the longest so you've won!" Then
Christopher Robin gave him his prize.
A big bouncy ball. "Oh, goody!
Tiggers love balls!" Tigger said happily.

"Did Tigger join in the games
after that?" asked Pooh.
"Yes, he really enjoyed
himself," said Christopher

Robin with a smile. "Good,
because games are fun
even if you don't win,"
yawned Pooh.

# Counting with Owl

# Drawing with Piglet

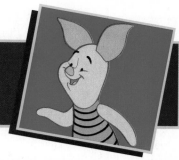

Can you help Piglet finish drawing the candles on Pooh's birthday cake?

# Birthday rhyme

Happy birthday to you,
Happy birthday to you,
Happy birthday dear Pooh Bear,
Happy birthday to you!

● When is it your birthday?

● How many cards is Piglet holding?

22

● How many balloons can you see?

Hope you have lots of fun,
And lots of presents, too,
And a lovely big birthday cake,
Especially for you!

● What is Pooh eating?

# In training

**1** "I think I'd better start training for Sports Day this afternoon," said Pooh. So he picked up a stick and set off through the Hundred Acre Wood.

**2** Soon he met Rabbit doing some press-ups. "18, 19, 20!" puffed Rabbit. "Why are you doing that?" asked Pooh. "I'm training for the races," said Rabbit.

**3** "I'm training, too," said Pooh. And off he went. Rabbit stared at him, confused. "Why is Pooh holding that stick?" he thought.

4 A little further on, Pooh met Tigger doing some star jumps. "Phew! I'm training for the races!" panted Tigger. "I want to make sure I win!"

5 "I'm training, too," said Pooh. "It's hard work!" And off he went, holding his stick. "Funny sort of training!" said Tigger, puzzled.

6 Then Pooh saw Piglet running on the spot. "I'm training for the races," Piglet told him. "So am I," said Pooh. "I'm practising keeping my arm still."

**7** It was almost time for the races to start, so the two friends set off. "We can train on the way," said Pooh.

**8** The first race was the egg and spoon race. Everyone lined up. "Ready, steady...go!" shouted Christopher Robin. And off they went.

**9** Tigger and Rabbit ran really fast. "I bet I win, I've been training!" boasted Tigger. "So have I!" cried Rabbit.

**10** But they kept dropping their eggs so they had to stop to pick them up again. Then Piglet dropped his egg, too.

**11** Pooh Bear walked slowly past them and right up to the winning line without dropping his egg at all. "Pooh's won!" cried Christopher Robin.

**12** "Well done," said Christopher Robin, giving Pooh a prize. "So that's why you were practising keeping your arm still!" smiled Piglet.

27

# Piglet's drawing page

**Join the dashes to see what prize Pooh won in the egg and spoon race.**

# Rabbit's maze

Rabbit's collecting flowers. Help him through the maze to his house and count how many flowers you collect along the way.

# Sports day rhyme

The race has just begun,
Here they are - watch them go!
See Tigger and Rabbit, off they run,
But Pooh is walking slow!

● **How many eggs can you count?**

● Who can you see in the picture?

Rabbit's dropped his egg,
Now Tigger's dropped his, too!
Who is left to win the race?
Well, I never! It's Pooh!

● What are they doing?

● What race do you like best?

# The pantomime

"Are you sitting comfortably, Pooh?" asked Christopher Robin. "Then I'll read you a little story..."

Rabbit had the good idea, one day, of putting on a pantomime. He decided that they should act out 'Jack and the Beanstalk'. For his play, he included Tigger, Pooh and Piglet and he invited Kanga, Owl and Roo to come and watch. Tigger was cast as the giant and was very excited! He couldn't wait to go on stage! Rabbit went on stage first to tell everyone the story. Tigger, though, was starting to get impatient! He poked his head around the curtains and whispered, "Is it my turn to go on stage yet?" "No! Piglet is on next," Rabbit whispered. "Go back!" So Tigger went backstage and waited. Next, Piglet who was Jack, went on to the stage. Then, it was Pooh's turn to go on stage. He was acting as Jack's mother. "What about me?" whispered Tigger, poking his head around the curtains again. "Isn't my turn to go on yet?" "No! The giant comes on later," said Rabbit. "Go back!" So, Tigger went backstage again and waited. At last, Piglet cried,

32

as Rabbit woke up Tigger. "Come on! It's your turn to go on stage!" he said. "Oh, goody," said Tigger, jumping up. How his friends clapped and cheered as he finally bounded on.

"Listen! I can hear a giant's footsteps!" This was Tigger's big moment! "Can you hear the giant?" Piglet asked the audience. But instead of giant footsteps, all everyone could hear were giant snores! "ZZZZZZZZZZZZ! ZZZZZZZZZZZZ!" Tigger had become so bored with waiting for his turn, he'd fallen asleep! Everyone giggled

"That's just like Tigger," said Pooh. "Did everyone like the pantomime?" "Oh, yes, they all really enjoyed it. And when it was finished, they all went to Kanga's for some tea and cake." said Christopher Robin. "I feel like eating some cake now!" said Pooh. "Come on, then," said Christopher Robin. "Let's go and get some!"

# Counting with Owl

● Are there two or three finger puppets?

● How many beans can you see?

● Can you see a mask?

**Help Rabbit through the beanstalk maze to reach Piglet. Count how many gold coins you collect on the way.**

How many gold coins are there altogether?

# Pantomime rhyme

"Christopher Robin's in trouble,"
Piglet told Winnie the Pooh,
We've got to save him from the giant,
But what on earth shall we do?

● Who can you see
in the picture?

● Have you been to
any pantomimes?

**What colour is Christopher Robin's shirt?**

So Piglet put on a scary mask,

To help scare the giant away,

But it was really only Tigger -

He was acting in a play!

# Tigger's go-kart

**1** Roo went to see Tigger, who was very busy. "What are you making?" asked Roo. "A super **go-kart** to whizz around in," said Tigger.

go-kart

very good

**2** "I'll just fix on this horn and it's finished," said Tigger. "It looks **very good**!" said Tigger, admiringly. "It's the best!" said Roo.

Bye

**3** "Now let's see how fast it goes!" said Tigger, jumping into the go-kart. "**Bye**! See you later!" he waved to Roo.

**4** Soon Tigger saw Eeyore. He sped past him, honking his horn. "**Surprise!**" he shouted. Eeyore jumped out of the way and into some thistles!

**5** "Ha, ha! That was funny!" chuckled Tigger. Then he saw Rabbit and decided to surprise him, too. "**Make way!**" he shouted, honking the horn loudly.

**6** Rabbit was so startled, he fell over, dropping his carrots everywhere! "**You fool!**" he shouted crossly as Tigger sped past, laughing.

**7** "Better slow down!" said Tigger as he sped down the hill towards the river. But he had forgotten to make any brakes for his kart! "I **can't stop**!" he shouted.

**8** Tigger's kart hit a rock at top speed! "**Help**!" cried Tigger as he sailed through the air and into the river.

**9** "Tigger was right, go-karts are **good fun**!" laughed Rabbit as Tigger sat soaking wet. "Bah!" said Tigger.

# Tigger's surprise

Tigger's here to show you how to make a super paper aeroplane. All you need is a piece of paper 21cm by 30cm and a grown-up to help.

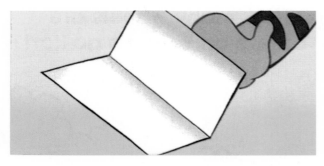

1) Fold the piece of paper in half lengthways.

2) Fold the top two corners down into the middle.

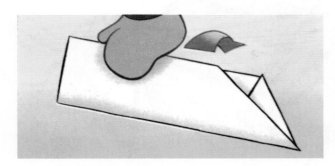

3) Fold the paper down the middle and press along the crease.

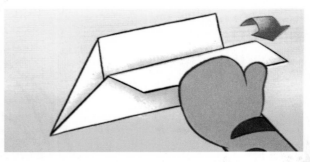

4) Fold each side of the paper to make the wings.

**Put a paper clip on the end and your plane is ready to fly! You can even colour in your plane if you want.**

# Piglet's colouring

How many wheels are there on Tigger's go-kart?

Who can you see in the picture?

Colour this picture with your crayons. Look at the little picture to see what colours to use.

What colour are Tigger's stripes?

What do you like to make?

# Mystery in the wood

"Are you sitting comfortably, pooh?" asked Christopher Robin. "Then I'll tell you a story..."

Pooh was walking through the Hundred Acre Wood, on his way to see his friend Eeyore, when he heard someone calling. "Look..Pooh! Look..Pooh!" Pooh looked around but he couldn't see anyone. "Is that you, Piglet?" he cried. No-one answered. So Pooh carried on walking. But as soon as he'd gone a couple of steps, someone called again. "Look...Pooh! Look...Pooh!"

Pooh stopped and looked. He still couldn't see anything. "Is that you, Tigger?" he called. No-one answered. "This is very peculiar," thought Pooh. He looked around one last time but he couldn't see anything so he carried on walking. But as soon

"He's shouting 'Cuckoo! Cuckoo!' not Look...Pooh!"

"He is?" asked Pooh. "Yes, look! There he is, on the branch of that tree," pointed Owl. Pooh looked up and saw a little grey bird. It opened his beak and shouted, "Cuckoo! Cuckoo!"

"See," said Owl. "Thank goodness for that," smiled Pooh. "Now I can go and see my friend Eeyore without having to stop and look every few steps!" And off he went through the wood, with the cuckoo shouting "Cuckoo! cuckoo!" after him.

as he'd gone a couple of steps, someone shouted to him again. "Look...Pooh! Look...Pooh!" Pooh stopped and looked around. No-one was there.

"Oh, dear! What am I supposed to be looking at?" he sighed. He looked everywhere, behind the bushes, under the leaves, amongst the plants. "What are you looking for, Pooh?" asked Owl, flying down beside him. Pooh stood up and scratched his head. "I don't know, Owl."

"Look...Pooh! Look...Pooh!" someone called again. "See, someone keeps calling 'Look Pooh', but I don't know what I'm supposed to be looking for," Pooh sighed.

Owl smiled. "Oh, Pooh, that's a cuckoo," he explained.

"But what was the cuckoo doing in the wood?" asked Pooh. "It came to stay for the summer months," said Christopher Robin. "When the summer's over, it will return home to a place called Africa." "That's a long way away, isn't it?" said Pooh. "Yes, it is," said Christopher Robin. "Well, I think I'll stay in the Hundred Acre Wood all year round!" laughed Pooh.

Are there three birds or two?

How many flowers can you see?

Can you count the lambs?

# Drawing with Piglet

Piglet needs help making this circle into a picture. He just doesn't know what to draw! Can you help him? Use one of the ideas here or make up a picture of your own!

**1** Tigger and Rabbit were walking past Christopher Robin's house when they saw a magic set that had been thrown away. "I'd like that!" said Tigger.

**2** Tigger picked up the box. "Now I can do lots of magic tricks!" he smiled. "There's no such thing as magic," grumbled Rabbit.

**3** "Yes, there is and I'm going to be Magic Tigger the Great Magician," said Tigger. Then off he bounced with the magic set.

4 Tigger was practising his magic when Piglet and Pooh came by. "Come and watch Magic Tigger do some fantastic tricks," announced Tigger.

5 Piglet and Pooh thought that sounded fun, so they stopped to watch. "Now I'm going to make some flowers appear in my hat!" said Tigger.

6 Tigger showed them the hat. "As you can see, there's nothing in there!" he said.

**7** Tigger put a cloth over the hat and waved his wand. "Abracadabra! Magic flowers appear!" he said. Piglet and Pooh watched eagerly.

**8** "And here are the flowers!" said Tigger, pulling off the cloth and putting his hand in the hat. But there were no flowers in there!

**9** "They must be here somewhere!" said Tigger, turning the hat upside down. "Piglet's gone, too!" said Pooh, looking around for his friend.

**10** "You've made him disappear!" said Pooh. "Oh dear, I must get him back," said Tigger. "Abracadabra, Piglet come back!" he said.

**11** "Here I am!" shouted Piglet, pulling the cloth off and holding a big bunch of flowers - Tigger had accidentally thrown them onto Piglet with the cloth!

**12** "Well done, Tigger!" said Pooh. "You've brought Piglet and the flowers back!" "Magic Tigger can magic anything!" smiled Tigger.

51

# Don't miss your favourite Disney characters in...

## Disney's Disney and Me

## Disney's Winnie the Pooh

## Disney's Princess

**Catch up with 101 Dalmatians, The Little Mermaid, The Lion King, Beauty and the Beast plus lots more!**

FREE Fridge Magnet!

Disney's Winnie the Pooh

The final part of your pull-out Time Chart inside!

Reading · Colouring · Puzzles

**Enter the magical and enchanting world of Disney's Princess!**

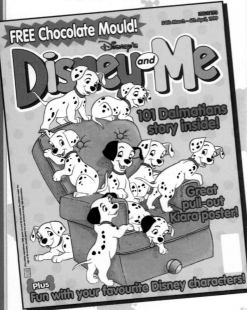

FREE Chocolate Mould!

Disney's Disney and Me

101 Dalmatians story inside!

Great pull-out Kiara poster!

Plus Fun with your favourite Disney characters!

**Follow Pooh, Piglet, Tigger, Roo and all the other friends in the Hundred Acre Wood!**

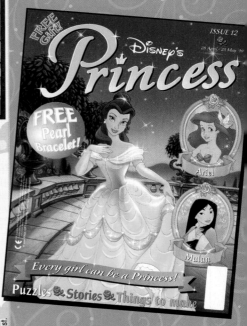

FREE Gift!

ISSUE 12
28 April – 25 May '99

Disney's Princess

FREE Pearl Bracelet!

Ariel

Mulan

Every girl can be a Princess!

Puzzles · Stories · Things to make

- Stories
- Puzzles
- Activities
- Posters
- Games

- Stories
- Activities
- Colouring
- Games
- Posters

- Stories
- Things to make
- Puzzles
- Quizzes
- Posters

**On sale every fortnight**

**On sale every four weeks**

**On sale every four weeks**

© Disney. Based on the Pooh stories by A. A. Milne © The Pooh properties Trust.

# Buy your copies now!

# Come see Disney's Millennium Celebrations

Win!

Win!

## at Walt Disney World. Resort
### IN FLORIDA

Win a fantastic holiday to
Walt Disney World® Resort in Florida!

There is an amazing party to celebrate the Millennium, starting on 1st October 1999 for 15 months at EPCOT®. Enter this competition to make sure you're in with a chance of joining in with all the fun!

You'll get to meet all your favourite Disney characters and there will be fantastic shows with lasers, fireworks, special effects and much, much more.

As well as **EPCOT®** you'll be able to visit Walt Disney World's other Theme Parks: **The Magic Kingdom®** Park, **Disney-MGM Studios, Disney's Animal Kingdom®** Theme Park and Disney's three wonderful **water parks**. It's a Disney dream come true!

## The Prize:

7 nights accommodation at a Walt Disney World® Resort Hotel for a family of 4 (one room for the winning family) and free entry to all 4 Walt Disney World® Theme Parks and 3 water parks. Prize includes return economy flights from Manchester or Gatwick to Orlando International or Sanford Airport. Meals are not included.

Send your answer, along with your name and address to:

Egmont World Ltd,
Deanway Technology Centre,
Wilmslow Road,
Handforth,
Cheshire SK9 3FB.

### How to enter:

Unscramble these letters to spell out a very famous Disney character: KIMCEY

**The closing date for entries is the 14th January 2000.**

### Terms and conditions
Please bear in mind the following points: Your holiday is provided subject to availability, and must be taken by 14th January 2001. Please check with your local authorities regarding your passport and visa requirements. Travel insurance is not included in your prize package. We strongly advise you take out travel insurance. Any costs incurred additional to the prize package elements listed (telephone charges, room service etc) are at guests' own expense. Transport to and from UK airport is not included. The prize winner if under 18 must be accompanied by an adult on the winning holiday. One winner will be chosen randomly from the total number of entries from this and three other Disney annuals. The winner will be notified by post. Judges' decision will be final and no correspondence shall be entered into. The winner's name will be made available on request from Egmont World Ltd, Deanway Technology Centre, Wilmslow Road, Handforth, Cheshire, SK9 3FB after 14th February 2000 - please enclose an SAE. Employees (and their relatives) of Egmont World Ltd and the Walt Disney Company Ltd and their associated companies are not eligible to enter. Entries are limited to one per person. Competition is open to residents of the UK, Ireland and the Channel Islands. The publishers reserve the right to vary prizes, subject to availability.

1 Rabbit saw a lovely, big conker hanging from a tree. But he couldn't reach it. "It's **too high**!" he sighed.

2 Tigger saw Rabbit trying to get the conker and offered to help. But he couldn't reach it either. "**I know** what to do," said Rabbit.

3 "You can lift me up," said Rabbit. "Then I can reach the conker." So that's what they did. "**Be careful**!" said Tigger.

4 "**Watch out!**" shouted Rabbit as Tigger started wobbling. But Tigger lost his balance and Rabbit fell back on top of him.

watch out

5 "Ow!" moaned Tigger and Rabbit as they lay on the ground. Just then Roo came along. "That's a **nice conker**!" he said.

nice conker

got it

6 Roo jumped up and grabbed the conker. "**Got it!**" he smiled, pulling it off the branch. Rabbit and Tigger couldn't believe it!

**7** Roo bounced off with the conker. Rabbit was so cross, he ran over and shook the tree. "Silly tree!" he shouted. "I wanted that conker!"

**8** Rabbit shook the tree so hard that all the conkers fell off a branch and hit him on the head. "Ouch!" he cried.

**9** "Well done, Rabbit!" smiled Tigger. "Now we've got a conker each!" Rabbit was very pleased. "Now we can have a conker match," he grinned.

# Tigger's surprise

Tigger's here to show you how to make a super fir cone owl. All you need is a fir cone, paper, round-ended scissors, glue and felt pens.

1) Draw the owl's eyes and beak on a piece of paper.

2) Now draw the owl's feet on another piece of paper.

3) Colour them in and cut them out with the scissors.

4) Glue them onto the fir cone to make a super owl.

# Autumn rhyme

An autumn storm
Came last night,
And blew Eeyore's house
Out of sight.

Who can you see
in the picture?

But Rabbit found it,
And so did Pooh,
Now Eeyore's house,
Is as good as new.

● What are they doing?

● How many logs can you see?

**Piglet is drawing a picture of Eeyore's house. Can you help him finish it? Then draw Rabbit's wheelbarrow next to it.**

# Rabbit's maze

With your finger, trace which fishing rod Rabbit should hold to catch the fish. Count how many frogs and water-lilies you pass on the way.